Storms inside My House

By Stacey A Saed

First Printing, 2023
ISBN 979-8-9877928-0-3

This book is dedicated to every child and adult who did not understand why the winds of dysfunction and addiction were ravaging their home life. If you have ever tried to pretend that all was well while you lived in fear and uncertainty, this book is for you.

I give thanks to my Divine Creator who said this needed to be written and allowed me to be the scribe.

I'm eternally grateful for my sons, Robert, Reid & Kieffer who are my greatest inspiration.

A special thank you to Jack & Samuel for giving me my first thumbs up review.

The weather reporter said, "It's a sunny day outside. It's a very pleasant day to be alive."

But from where I sat inside my home, the storm clouds were forming and I felt very alone.

It's confusing to look out my window and see the sun shining and the warm weather. Those things weren't happening IN my house.

The storms were starting and we were taking cover... hoping it would blow over soon.

My name is Natasha and my house is full of swirls, gusts and winds. Doors slam and sometimes things break. When the smells and yells begin in our house, my brothers and I know to take shelter in my room.

There are others who have storms inside their houses too. I can see it on the faces of my friends.
But we keep it a secret. We don't talk about those tornados and cloudy days.

We pretend it's sunny, like the man said on TV. We try to smile and laugh and play so they won't find out.

I was told I would get hurt if I told anyone. I was told to stay silent and out of the way. Sometimes I was told the storms are in my head and I made it up ... like a story.

One day, I saw two girls talking about their hard times. I thought that was brave. It made me feel brave too.

We found a safe grown up at school and began talking. It felt good to know there are others like me. We named our group The Stormacers, because we were learning to use our strengths over our storms at home.

The grown up we trusted told us about things other kids did to help them feel better.

LeAndrea had a flower bush she liked to visit and sniff the sweet smells. It helped her breathe and see beauty in nature.

Roderick liked to walk on rocks. He crisscrossed the same pattern over the stones. It helped him focus and collect his thoughts.

Peggy rode her horse Ransom. They liked to jump rivers and fences. He was a good listener when she whispered her secrets in his ear. It helped her feel free and alive.

Mateo was quiet and liked to paint alone. The colors and paintings and paintings help him feel hopeful.

Olivia liked to sit in the library surrounded by books and read. She could become smarter by learning as she relaxed.

Anthony acted in plays at school. The kids were nice and it made him feel fearless and seen.

I closed my eyes and thought about what would make me happy. I took deep breaths and imagined places I could live. There was happiness on the inside no matter what was going on the outside.

Soon other children with stormy houses told a safe grown up and got a few good tips...

- Find a safe space if you are able.

- Pray

- Breathe deeply.

- Ask for help from people you can trust like a counselor, a teacher, a friend's mom or dad.

- Imagine a "happy place."

- Keep the faith that you will survive and there are better days ahead.

- Take it one day at a time.

- Do something kind for another person.

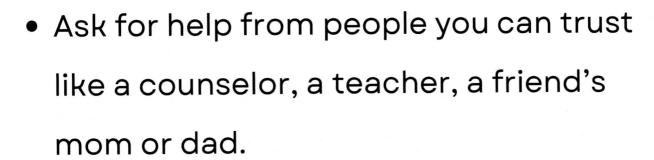

It wasn't always easy and it wasn't always hard. There were stormy days and sunny days ahead. And together "The Stormacers" were going to be okay!

Natasha

Roderick

Olivia

Meet

the

STORMACERS

Anthony

Mateo

Peggy & Ransom

LeAndrea

About the Author

Stacey A Saed

Stacey is a mother, artist, author and a grateful member of the recovery community. Her personal experience and the experiences of others provided the truth telling found in this book.

The Stormacers group of survivors is a movement not a moment. Her hope is to see this publication in the hands of any child who needs it.

Made in the USA
Columbia, SC
24 March 2023

14140747R00024